CHALLENGE!

Fun With Puzzles, Riddles,

Word Games, and Problems

By Charlie Rice

Illustrated by Walter Swartz

♛ Hallmark Editions

CONTENTS

Challenge!

QUIZZES TO BEGIN WITH

Number 1: The "Easy" Quiz

When you glance at the questions below, you might very well say that it's not worth your while to answer them—that even a child could pass such a quiz.

But try it anyway, just for the fun of it. This "easy" quiz was pretested on several dozen well-educated people—their average score was two and a half correct answers out of 10. If you can score three right, you're really good. Four right? You're in the genius class!

1. Who and/or what chased Eliza onto the ice in the novel "Uncle Tom's Cabin"?

2. What color is steam?

3. You buy a railroad ticket marked "Good For One Year Only." You pay one dollar for it. How long is it worth a dollar?

4. Violin strings are made of the gut of what animal?

5. Can you name two national legal holidays designated by Congress?

6. What relation is Jacqueline Kennedy to Ethel Kennedy (the wife of Robert F. Kennedy)?

7. What was the first year of our 20th century?

8. What was the volcanic material that buried the city of Pompeii?

9. You are in the process of buying a house and you meet with your local banker, your real estate agent and your lawyer. One of the group says, "I will give you a $10,000 mortgage on the house." Who says it?

10. In the name Jeanne d'Arc (Joan of Arc), what does the "d'Arc" mean?

a. "Of Arc" (The village she was brought up in).

b. "Of the Ark" (Biblical allusion).

c. "d'Arc" (because her parents were Mr. & Mrs. d'Arc).

d. "Of the Arch" (referring to a triumphal arch).

Answers on page 48.

Number 2: The "Hard" Quiz

Only an expert could answer any of the questions below, but you'll be surprised how well you will do. In fact, this hard quiz is guaranteed to produce at least a passing, if not a brilliant, score.

1. Which of the following organizations was not founded in America?

a. The Boy Scouts   b. The Red Cross

c. The Salvation Army

2. If you were writing a letter to the President of the United States, which of these salutations would you choose as being correct?

a. The President: b. Mr. President:

c. My Dear Mr. President:

3. Which of these two famous scientists originated the "Theory of Evolution"?

a. Charles Darwin   b. Alfred Wallace

4. Which of the names below is **not** a geographical place?

a. Island of Reil   b. McBurney's Point

c. Tunnel of Corti

5. Which of these cities has a population of 126,706?

a. Rockford, Ill.   b. Madison, Wis.

Answers on page 49.

SEEING IS BELIEVING—OR IS IT?

The timeworn phrase, "Seeing is believing," has gone the way of the horse and buggy. Science disagrees. Entire books have been written about the effects on your vision of certain combinations of lines, angles, colors and curves—and much of modern art and architecture draws its vigor and beauty from the fact that the eye can be tricked.

One of the simplest and best optical illusions is "Abe Lincoln's Hat." The problem is to guess how much taller the crown of Abe's hat is than the width of the brim.

Well, the truth is that the crown is precisely as high as the brim is wide! Measure the hat if you don't believe me.

For a really baffling optical illusion, try the "Old Roman Pitchfork." The problem is this:
How many prongs, or "tines," has this old Roman pitchfork?

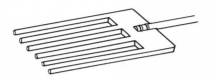

When you first look at it you will probably say six. But now cover the left-hand side of the pitchfork so that none of the prong-ends are visible—then estimate how many prongs there are. You will say four. Where did the other prongs go?—I don't know either!

Now try to solve these problems:

1. Which is longer, AX or AY?

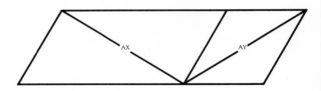

The Mysterious Lady

Guess the age of the lady you see in this picture. Now look again closely and see if you can see another lady of quite a different age.

Amateur psychologists can have a heyday with this illusion!

Answer on page 50.

PUZZLES, PUZZLES

Can you imagine a bunch of staid grown-ups playing with blocks? I saw it happen once, on Park Av-
enue in New York. The occasion was a puzzle ex-
hibition, and after watching for a while, I under-
stood why such a crowd had gathered.

Here are some of the puzzles that struck me as
fun:

1. What time is it?

2. The following letters are the initial letters of the
words of a common sequence that even the small-
est school child knows by heart. Fill in the missing
initial letter of the last word:

OTTFFSSEN—

3.   64   48
The wrong answer to this question is right: Which
of the above numbers cannot be divided by two?

14

4.

Name each of the above figures. If you are correct, the initial letters of your answers will tell you so!

5. What is the total weight of a fish if it weighs ten pounds plus half its weight?

6. A rope ladder hangs over the side of a ship so that the ladder just reaches the water. The rungs are nine inches apart. How many rungs will be under water when the tide has risen three feet?

7. Define each of the following by a single letter. If you're right, you'll know it!

A. Blue and white bird

B. Lowest note on the piano

C. Large body of water

D. Girl's nickname

E. Vegetable

F. Exclamation

G. Beverage

8. Fred Williamson and his wife went to a horse race. As the horses sped around the oval track, Mrs. Williamson remarked, "I'm getting confused trying to watch all the horses at once, so I think I'll just watch the one whose jockey is wearing red. Why, I can't even tell how many horses are in this race." "I just counted them," said Mr. Williamson, "and I noticed that the number is the total of one-third of the horses in front of the red horse, plus three-fourths of those behind it."

How many horses were in the race?

9. Mr. Nickerson, a precise, domineering office manager who hated excessive discussion, over-heard the following dialogue, on his office phone.

Voice: "Is Mr. Nickerson there?"

Secretary: "Who's calling, please?"

Voice: "Rhett."

Sec: "I beg your pardon?"

Voice: "Rhett. R as in Rhinoceros, H as in Hippo-potamus, E as in Egret, ——"

Sec: "E as in what, sir?"

Voice: "E as in Egret, T as in Tiger, and another T as in Tiger. R, H, E, T, T, Rhett."

Sec: "Thank you, sir. I'll see if Mr. Nickerson is in."

Why did Nickerson criticize his secretary?

Answers on page 51.

WORDLES—

WORD PUZZLES
TO TRAP YOU

How far can a dog run into the woods?

That's the kind of question people rage over. I wouldn't ask it of anyone. But in case you're wondering:

A dog can run halfway into the woods. From then on, he's running out of the woods.

Settled again? Think about this riddle, then, which a friend of mine tried on me one day:

A farmer had seventeen jackasses and all but nine of them died. How many did he have left?

I answered my friend politely, "Nine jackasses,

unless you want to count yourself."

That pretty much did it for me. I decided to collect a rage of riddles, and turned up a fair number that fooled me and some old-timers that tickle me. Here they are, with answers at the end if you require them:

1. Is there any Federal law against a man's marrying his widow's sister?

2. If you had only one match and entered a cold room that contained a kerosene lamp, an oil heater, and a wood stove, what would you light first for maximum heat?

3. How many animals of each species did Moses take aboard the Ark with him before the great flood?

4. The Yankees and the Tigers play five baseball games. They each win three. No tie or disputed games were involved. How come?

5. How many birthdays does the average man have? The average woman?

6. According to international law, if an airplane should crash on the exact border between two countries, would unidentified survivors be buried in the country they were traveling **to,** or the country they were traveling **from?**

7. An archeologist claims he has dug up a coin that is clearly dated 46 B.C. Why is he a liar?

Answers on page 52.

And More

For those of you who still aren't satisfied, here are more wordles:

8. What is one thing positively which lions have that no other animal has or can have?

9. What can speak every language in the world?

10. What is the word that almost everyone pronounces wrong?

11. Kansas City and St. Louis are 240 miles apart. A train leaves Kansas City traveling at 60 miles an hour; another leaves St. Louis at the same time, traveling at 40 miles an hour. Which will be farther from St. Louis when they meet?

12. If a man is on top of a mountain with a live goose in his arms, what is the quickest way for him to get down?

13. What's the most important use for cowhide?

14. Why is it bad to go skating on an empty stomach?

15. Why are people so tired on April 1st?

16. What is the beginning of eternity,
The end of time and space,
The beginning of every end,
And the end of every race?

17. If a horse had a rope 6 yards long tied around its neck and there was a bag of oats 25 feet away, could the horse reach the oats to eat them?

Answers on page 53.

RIDDLES FOR REAL

Youngsters seem to go through a stage of constantly posing riddles to their parents. School chums seem to be their major source, and that's probably the reason some of the riddles are so baffling to us older folks!

Anyhow, I got to remembering some pretty good ones from my own past—not the silly ones this time, but the real brain-twisters—and here's a sampling:

1. A man and his sister were walking together. The woman pointed across the street to a boy, and said: "That boy is my nephew." The man replied, "He is not **my** nephew."

Can you explain this paradox?

2. Two fathers and two sons own 21 horses. They

are each moving to different parts of the country and want to divide their horses evenly among them. Is this possible? How?

3. Two rabid baseball fans went to see a 4th of July doubleheader on passes from the management. In spite of the fact that they were given excellent box seats on the third-base line, they persisted in cheering for the visiting team all afternoon. This bit of rudeness might have been explained on sentimental grounds, since one fan happened to have the same name as the visiting third baseman, Bill Jones, and the other the same name as the visiting pitcher, Jim Smith. But what really needs explaining is the fact that they did not take off their hats when the national anthem was played—even though it was Independence Day. How come?

4. Two miners had been working in a coal mine and came up after the day's work—one with a nice clean face, the other with a very dirty one. When they said goodnight, the clean-faced one hurried to a wash basin where he scrubbed his face vigorously, while the grimy one went his way just as he was. Why?

5. A man builds an ordinary house with four sides, except that each side has a southern exposure. A bear comes up and knocks on the door. What color is the bear?

6. A man lived on the 12th story of an apartment

building. Each day, when he came home from work, he took the elevator to the 8th floor, got out and walked to his apartment on 12. The elevator was in good operating order and went all the way to the 12th floor. Why did the man walk up those four flights of stairs?

7. A thief stole a string of nine pearls. Later he was told that one of the pearls was only paste. He knew that the fake pearl would be lighter than the others and decided to find out which one it was. After weighing the pearls on a balance scale **only twice,** he knew which pearl was made of paste. How did he find out?

8. My cousin wants to drive, via the shortest route possible, from Miami to New York to see a specialist about his laryngitis. To do so, however, is not easy. Some distance out of town the main road forks into two roads, neither of which is marked by a road sign. One of the roads will take him directly to New York, but the other will lead far out of the way. To make matters worse, there are only two people living near the fork who could tell him which one to take. The two people are identical twins in every respect, except that one twin always tells the truth, and the other always lies. As my cousin feels his laryngitis is worsening, he wants to save his voice by asking one of the twins only **one** question to determine which is the proper road to

New York. What is the **one** question he can ask which will absolutely disclose to him the road which leads to his destination?

9. Three missionaries and three cannibals come to a river and desire to cross. The boat will only carry two people. All the missionaries can row, but only one of the cannibals can. The trips must be arranged so that the cannibals will never outnumber the missionaries. How can this be done?

10. The story is told that Alexander the Great once needed a man of great subtlety for an important espionage mission. Unable to choose from among his three brightest spies, he summoned them all to his conference tent and had them blindfolded. Then he put a skullcap on the head of each one and said:

"Each of you now wears either a black or a white skullcap. When I remove the blindfolds, raise your hand as soon as you see a black skullcap. Then drop your hand as soon as you know the color of your own cap."

The blindfolds were removed, and all three spies raised their hands at once, for the wily Alexander had put a black cap on each spy's head. After a few minutes one spy dropped his hand and said, correctly, "My cap is black." By what logical reasoning had he determined Alexander's ruse?

Answers on page 54.

PICK-UP TRICKS

"Pick-up sticks" was a favorite childhood game of mine. If you think that game was intriguing, try these pick-up tricks at a party sometime!

1. Using **all** of the original matchsticks, and rearranging only two of them, make four equal squares out of the following configuration:

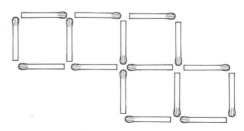

2. Draw the two figures below, using only one un-broken and un-retraced line for each one:

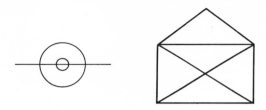

3. Divide this figure below into four equal and identically shaped parts:

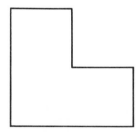

4. Move one match and make a square.

5. Take away eight toothpicks so there are only two squares left.

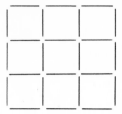

6. If you had a 64-square checkerboard and a bunch of rectangular blocks that would each cover two of the checkerboard squares, could you possibly arrange the blocks on the board in such a way that they covered every square except those in two opposite corners?

Answers on page 57.

FIDGETY-DIGITS: FUN WITH NUMBERS

Common numbers are intriguing to scientists and mathematicians. But they also fascinate the rest of us when used peculiarly or in combination with familiar problems—as the following bits of fun demonstrate.

1. A snail at the bottom of a forty-foot telephone pole crawls upwards at the rate of three feet per day, but falls down two feet every night. How many days will it take the snail to reach the top of the pole?

2. How can you write the number one hundred with eight nines?

3. If it takes 3 1/2 minutes to fry one egg, how long does it take to fry four eggs?

4. A college boy found himself so broke that he had to conserve words when he wired his parents to send him more money. If each letter in the addition stands for a number, how much money did the following wire ask for?

$$
\begin{array}{r}
\text{SEND} \\
+\text{MORE} \\
\hline
\text{MONEY}
\end{array}
$$

5. This sounds impossible, but it can be done: Take one from twenty-nine and leave thirty.

6. Two Samaritans, one with five loaves of bread and the other with three, stopped by the roadside to eat. A third traveler arrived before they began their meal, and asked that the first two share their food with him. They readily consented, and the three travelers shared the food equally. When he had finished, the third traveler arose, thanked the other two for the bread, and left eight shekels in payment for his meal.

The Samaritan who originally had five loaves of bread thought the eight coins should be divided five to him and three to the other—in the same proportion as their original and respective quantities of bread. The other Samaritan, however, thought the coins should be split four and four, since all the bread had been equally shared. Unable to agree on the matter, the two Samaritans took their case to a local arbiter, who decided that the man who originally had five loaves should receive seven shekels, and the man who originally had three loaves receive one shekel.

On what reasoning was the arbiter's judgment based?

7. Three insurance men were traveling across country on their way to a convention. The first night they stopped at a motel. The clerk told them they could have a room for three for $30, which they accepted. After the men had retired to the room, however, the clerk discovered he had made a mistake, and that the room was only $25 for one night. He therefore gave $5 to a bellboy and told him to return it to the three men. When the bellboy returned the money, the men gave him a $2 tip so that they could easily divide the remainder equally among them.

Consequently, each of the insurance men ended up paying only $9 for the room. The total was therefore $27. The bellboy got $2. What happened to the other dollar?

Answers on page 59.

The Million Dollar Shoes

A cowhand once took his horse to the blacksmith for shoeing, and was shocked to learn that the job would cost him $50.

The cowhand was indignant. "Fifty dollars!? That's outrageous! I will not pay you that for shoeing my horse."

The blacksmith scratched his head, and then asked, "If you won't pay me $50, then will you pay me a penny for the first nail, two cents for the second, four cents for the third, eight cents for the fourth, and so on. . . . for all thirty-two nails I must use?"

The cowpoke thought to himself, "What a chump! That won't be anywhere near $50."—"I'll take you up on your second price," he said to the blacksmith.

When the cowhand came back to get his horse the next day, he found that indeed the bill was nowhere near $50. He fainted away when he saw that the amount was. . . .

$42,949,672.95! ! ! !

If you don't believe it, try it and see!

Just multiply 2 x 2 31 times, then add to that product the product of each multiplication along the way (or multiply 2 x 2 32 times and subtract 1).

Magic Numbers

An unusual party trick: Ask one of your guests to

write down any three-digit number, and then to repeat the digits in the same order to make a six-digit number (**e.g.,** 465,465). With your back turned so that you cannot see the number, ask another guest to take the number and divide it by 7—again concealing the figures from you.

Tell him not to worry about there being a remainder to the division, because there won't be any. He'll be surprised to find you're right.

Now ask a third guest to take the number resulting from the division (still unknown to you) and divide it by 11. Once again you state that there will be no remainder to worry about.

With your back still turned, and no knowledge of the figures obtained by these computations, have still another guest divide the last result by 13. Again the division comes out even. This final result is written down on a piece of paper and handed to you folded so that you cannot see it. Without opening it, pass the paper to the person who thought of the original number, and tell him that it is the number he first wrote down. And it is!

Answer on page 59.

PROBABLE PROBABILITIES

Bet a friend even money that if he writes down five letters of the alphabet, you can guess at least one of the letters if you are given five chances. Most people would be glad to bet you. After all, there are 26 letters in the alphabet, which seemingly gives you only about one chance in five of guessing one of the letters that they write down. Actually, the chances are two-to-one in your favor, and you can play it with a whole roomful of people. Each one can write down his own list, and with the same five-guess list of your own you can win two out of three bets.

Want to test it out? Okay, get a pencil and jot down five letters, completely at random. Then compare your five "guesses" with the six random lists of letters printed below. With ordinary luck, you'll find that you've guessed a correct letter in four out of the six lists.

1. C R S Y O
2. M K A J T
3. B C E X L
4. N A P O Z
5. D G F E T
6. H Q I U W

"Doop"

We ran into a new game called "Doop," and we haven't been quite the same since we played it. Try it and see.

Our host asked the twelve of us each to write down a specific playing card—queen of clubs, two of diamonds, or anything that came to mind. So we all did, and then he said he'd bet anyone a dime that at least two people had written down the same card. After a bit of discussion, every one of us took him up. After all, we reasoned, there were 52 cards in the deck and only 12 of us.

So we promptly lost a dime apiece! Two had written down the 10 of spades.

The host next asked us to count the exact amount of change we had on our persons. When we had written the amount down, he offered to bet that at least two people would have precisely the same sum. This time only a few inveterate suckers took him up.

And they lost! Two had precisely 87 cents.

Next we found that among 12 people, two had fathers named Frank and two had mothers named Louise, and two were born in the same hospital in St. Louis. Two were left-handed, two had the same street number, and two owned Dalmatian dogs.

Small world, isn't it?

And sort of scary, until you understand what the game of DOOP is based upon: a fascinating mathematical principle of duplication. Some Doops can be figured precisely (such as the playing-card one); others must be figured on estimate (such as amount of change in pocket).

The chances of duplication among any considerable gathering of people are much greater than you would dream—and soar rapidly with each added guest.

Example: If you have 28 guests at a party, the chances are almost two-to-one that two guests will have the same birthday! If you don't believe it, ask a mathematician—he'll tell you why.

$$1 - \frac{365!}{(365-N)!} \frac{1}{365^N}$$

is the formidable mathematical formula for finding the probability that at least two people will have the same birthday in a crowd of N (the number present) people. It works out that the chance of at least two people in 23 having the same birthday is a little over 50-50—.507 probability, to be exact.

The mathematician will also warn you that the law of averages isn't always reliable, and that sometimes a Doop stunt won't work. But on the other hand, sometimes you'll get more spectacular results than you had hoped for—two or three duplications when you expect only one.

In any case, Doop is a great icebreaker for parties, and here are a few suggestions, based on the number of people in your party:

PARTY OF SIX.

You should get at least one Doop if your guests write down:

Month of birth

Choice of a card in any one suit

Choice of positions on a football team

Number of coins in pocket or purse

(The Magic Number for a Party of Six is 23, meaning the limit of choices you can offer and still expect a duplication. Make up your own Doop stunts by thinking of lists of familiar objects not exceeding 23.)

PARTY OF EIGHT.

Date of month they were born

Choice of letters in the alphabet

Choice of amendments to the Constitution

(Magic Number is 43)

PARTY OF TWELVE.

Choice of any card in the deck

Exact amount of change in pocket or purse

Choice of any state in the union

Exact weight of each guest

Choice of any white key on the piano

(Magic Number for 12 is 99)

PATENTED PLEASURES

The U.S. Patent Office handles thousands upon thousands of new patents annually, and most of them are decidedly practical and businesslike. But Americans have always been an inventive people, and as long as there are inventors there will be unusual inventions that almost defy description.

The fun of "Patented Pleasures," which begins on the next page, is in figuring out what the inventor intended his invention to be. After you do that, you may want to mull over some other questions, such as what kind of personal difficulty led the inventor to his bright idea—and who would patent such crazy notions in the first place! Maybe the patents here will give you an idea for a patent of your own.

1. Bowler hat contains:

    a. Miniature guided missiles . . . .[   ]

    b. Cleverly-concealed cigars . . . .[   ]

    c. Portable hair curlers . . . .[   ]

2. Shapely creature is:

    a. Cow with freezer compartment . . . . [   ]

    b. Unique hunting decoy . . . . [   ]

    c. Symbol of famous corporation . . . . [   ]

3. Patent is for:

    a. Scaring visiting enemies . . . . [   ]

    b. Sit-down shower bath . . . . [   ]

    c. Air-conditioned rocking chair . . . . [   ]

4. Lady with a caster is:

    a. Fancy ball-point pen ....[   ]

    b. Untiring cocktail hostess ....[   ]

    c. Excellent dancing partner ....[   ]

5. Man is wearing:

   a. Personal salad bowl ....[   ]

   b. Sunshade ....[   ]

   c. Smog and fallout deflector ....[   ]

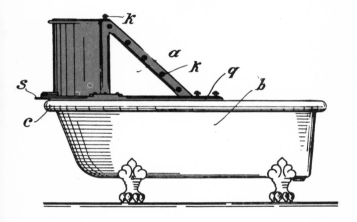

6. Object on bathtub is:

a. Stepladder for toe-testing . . . . [   ]

b. Adult's toy sailboat . . . . [   ]

c. Sauna attachment . . . . [   ]

Answer on page 60.

Mystery Quiz

Psychologists are forever mumbling into their beards about popular quizzes. The questions, they complain, always tip the reader off as to what he's supposed to say.

Well, here's a quiz that critics can't mumble about! I'm not going to tell you what it's all about till you've taken it. Grab a pencil and write in the answers as fast as you can. Don't worry if you have to leave some answers blank. The only rule is don't peek at the answers till you've finished.

Answers on page 60.

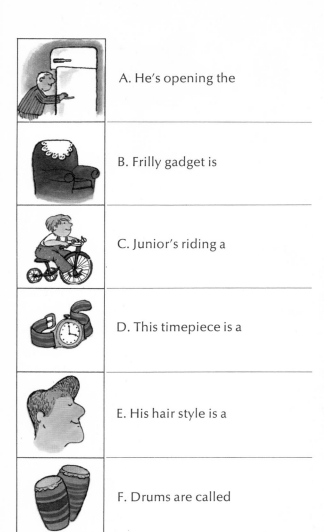

A. He's opening the

B. Frilly gadget is

C. Junior's riding a

D. This timepiece is a

E. His hair style is a

F. Drums are called

G. These golf-pants are

H. This machine is a

I. They're sitting in a

J. Cop is twirling a

K. What's this called?

L. What style of tie?

Answers on page 60.

ANSWERS

Answers to Number 1: The "Easy" Quiz

1. Poor Eliza was running from a slave trader named Haley. Simon Legree had nothing to do with it, nor were there any bloodhounds involved. The dogs were the invention of theatrical troupes that dramatized "Uncle Tom's Cabin" and played it throughout America.

2. True steam is an invisible gas; the white stuff is condensed water vapor that is formed as a result of steam cooling off rapidly.

3. If you have not used the ticket, it is worth a dollar indefinitely, or at least until recovery is barred by the statute of limitations.

4. Violin strings are made of sheep intestines and probably always have been.

5. There are no national legal holidays as such in the U.S. because Congress has no power to proclaim them. All holidays are established by the several states.

6. Mrs. Kennedy is not Ethel Kennedy's sister-in-law. Ethel Kennedy is merely the wife of Mrs. Kennedy's brother-in-law, Robert F. Kennedy. "In-law" relationships do not extend a second step.

7. The first year of the 20th century was 1901. The 1st century started with the year 1, and the century is not finished until the last day of the 100th year.

8. Pompeii was buried by a rain of stone and ash, not lava.

9. The one who says "I'll give you a $10,000 mortgage on the house" has to be you yourself. Bankers do not give mortgages—they **take** mortgages. A mortgage is security for a loan. You give the banker a mortgage, he gives you a loan.

10. Jeanne d'Arc's name did not come from her native village. There was no such village near Domremy, where she was born. She took her last name, just as every other girl does, from her parents, Mr. and Mrs. Jacques d'Arc.

Answers to Number 2: The "Hard" Quiz

1. Any answer is right. Though the organizations all sound 100 percent American, the Boy Scouts was founded in England in 1907 by Lord Baden-Powell, the Red Cross in Switzerland in 1864 by Henri Dunant, and the Salvation Army in England in 1865 by William Booth.

2. All three are acceptable.

3. Either answer is correct. By an almost incredible coincidence, both Darwin and Wallace formulated the theory at the same time and presented their findings to the scientific world in a joint report. The only reason we speak of the "Darwin Theory" is that, later on, Darwin wrote his "Origin of The Species," a book that became famous.

4. Any answer is correct. All three are parts of the body. The Island of Reil (after physiologist Johann

49

C. Reil) is a point in the brain. McBurney's Point (after surgeon Charles McBurney) is the point where the incision for an appendectomy is made. The Tunnel of Corti (after anatomist Alfonso Corti) is a part of the ear.

5. Either answer is correct. According to the 1960 census, both Rockford, Ill., and Madison, Wis., had precisely the same population.

Aren't you glad you're a genius?

Answers to Seeing Is Believing—Or Is It?

1. The lines, unbelievably, are of the same length.
2. Fish pole A caught the fish—as you can prove to yourself with a ruler or straightedge.
3. You can see a little cube in a corner, or a big cube with a little cube cut out of one corner, or a big cube with a little cube sticking out of a corner.
4. The five-pointed, symmetrical star is upright near the lower right-hand corner of the square. One point touches the edge of the square.
5. The word is FLY—formed by the spaces between the dark shapes.

Answer to the Mysterious Lady

The mysterious lady is really two ladies in one!

There is a young, pretty girl wearing a necklace who has the left side of her face turned to you.

And there is an old woman huddled up in her

coat whose face is larger and more disclosed.

Which did you see first? Can you see the other one now? As you get used to the picture, can you see them both?

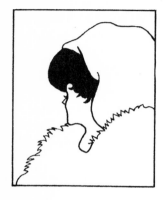 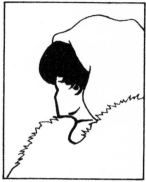

Answers to Puzzles, Puzzles

1. The time is 9:25. It's a mirror image.

2. One, Two, Three, Four, Five, Six, Seven, Eight, Nine, **Ten.**

3. The only possible answer is **both.** The answer to the question **as put** is "neither," since neither 64 nor 48 can**not** be divided by two. Therefore, if "neither" is the right answer but the **wrong** answer is right, "both" must be the answer.

4. Cube, Octagon, Rectangle, Rhomboid, Equilateral, Circle, Trapezoid: the initial letters spell CORRECT.

5. Twenty pounds.

If the fish's weight equals ten-pounds-plus-half-its-weight, then half its weight must also equal ten pounds—therefore, its full weight is 20 pounds. Algebraically:

W=full weight of fish

W=10 lbs. + 1/2W

1/2W = 10 lbs.

W = 20 lbs.

6. None of the rungs would be under water. Ship and ladder both rise with the tide.

7. J-A-C-K-P-O-T!

8. There were thirteen horses in the race. Since the track is a continuous oval, each other horse is both in front of and behind the one with the jockey in red. One-third of twelve—four—plus three-fourths of twelve—nine—equals thirteen.

9. Nickerson's secretary obviously knew the third letter of Rhett's name, since she said it when she asked "E as in what?" She did not need to know what, she only needed to know the letter. For this small error the mean Nickerson criticized her.

Answers to Wordles—Word Puzzles to Trap You

1. There's no law against a man's marrying his widow's sister, but it would be the neatest trick of the week. To have a widow, he'd have to be dead.

2. First of all, you'd light the match.

3. Moses took no animals at all, since he had no Ark. Noah took quite a few.

4. Who said that the Yankees and the Tigers were playing against **each other** in those games?

5. The average man has one birthday, the average woman also. All the rest are birthday **anniversaries.**

6. You can't bury survivors under **any law**—unless they don't have strength enough to object!

7. The archeologist is a liar because B.C., of course, means Before Christ, and who could have guessed in advance when Christ would be born?

And More Answers

8. Baby lions.

9. An echo.

10. "Wrong."

11. When the trains meet, they will obviously be the same distance from **anywhere!**

12. Pluck the goose!

13. Holding cows together.

14. It's okay, but ice is better!

15. Because they have just finished a 31-day March.

16. The letter E.

17. Why, sure—if the other end of the rope isn't tied to anything!

Answers to Riddles for Real

1. The boy is the man's son.

2. There are only three owners: The two fathers are a grandfather and a father, and the two sons are that same father and his son. Therefore, each gets seven horses.

3. The two baseball fans were Mrs. Bill Jones and Mrs. Jim Smith, wives of the visiting players. Passes are always available to players' wives, and ladies need not take their hats off when the national anthem is played, even on the Fourth of July.

4. Each assumed his face looked like the other's.

5. The bear that knocked on the door would have to be a white polar bear, because the only place you could build a house with four southern exposures is at the North Pole, where every direction is south.

6. The man had no choice: he was a midget, and could reach no farther up than the elevator button for the 8th floor.

7. The jewel thief placed three pearls on one side of the balance scale and three on the other side. If these two bunches weighed the same, then the fake pearl was one of the remaining three. If one of the bunches was lighter than the other, then that bunch had the paste pearl in it. Having discovered which threesome had the fake pearl, he then placed one pearl from those three on one side of the scale and one on the other. If they weighed the same, he knew that the remaining pearl was false. If their weights were different, he knew that the lighter pearl was made of paste.

8. My cousin can ask either twin, "If I asked your brother which road leads to New York, what would his answer be?" The dishonest twin, knowing his brother always tells the truth, would lie, naming the **wrong** road. The honest brother, knowing his brother always lies, would truthfully tell his brother's lie—again, naming the **wrong** road. In either case, my cousin would know he had been misdirected and would take the other road from the one either brother told him—the **right** road.

9. The cannibal who can row (Cannibal R) takes over one cannibal and leaves him. He then takes another cannibal over and leaves him with the first. When Cannibal R returns with the boat, two missionaries go over, one of them remaining on the other side while the rowing missionary returns bringing a cannibal with him. One missionary then goes over with Cannibal R. A missionary then returns with a cannibal, but leaves Cannibal R on the other side. The two missionaries then cross over and give the boat to Cannibal R, who makes two other trips over for the cannibals, bringing one at a time.

10. The brainy spy said: "I rapidly calculated that

there were seven possible combinations of black and white caps. For example, we could all be wearing white caps—but then no one would have raised his hand. Two could be wearing white caps —but then the spy with the black cap would see the others' hands raised but would himself see no black cap, and would instantly deduce that his own cap must be black. Or my colleagues, A and B, could be wearing black caps, I a white cap—but A would instantly realize that if B has raised his hand it must be because A's cap is black, since he also could see my cap and my cap, in this proposition, is white.

"I worked rapidly through these combinations and had sufficient respect for my colleagues to assume that they were thinking along the same lines. But in the meantime **all our hands continued to be raised.** Then an eighth combination occurred to me, a wily Alexandrian combination that would leave us all in exactly the indecisive state we were exhibiting—and that is, that **all three caps were black.** For this sly arrangement is the **only** arrangement whereby no one of us could immediately deduce the color of his cap from the action of the others. And so I lowered my hand, knowing my cap to be black."

Answers to Pick-Up Tricks

1.

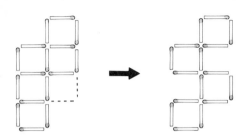

2.

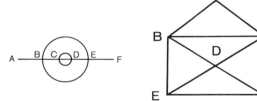

A B E D C D C B E F

or

A B E B C D C D E F

E D F E B D C B A C F

or

E B A C F B C E F

3.

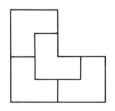

4.

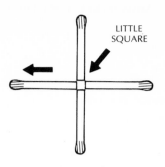

LITTLE
SQUARE

5.

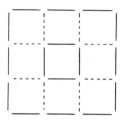

6. No, you could not. Since every dark square on a checkerboard is adjacent to a lighter square on any side, a block which covers two squares must ALWAYS cover both a light and a darker square. Since the number of dark squares in a checkerboard is equal to the number of light squares, and since the opposite corners of the board are the same color, the problem as proposed is impossible.

Answers to Fidgety-Digits

1. Thirty-eight days. He reaches the top of the pole the last day.

2. 99 $\underline{999}$
999

3. 3 1/2 minutes, provided all four eggs are fried in the same pan at the same time.

4. $ 95.67
$\underline{+10.85}$
$106.52

5. From Roman XXIX take I and leave XXX.

6. The arbiter reasoned that each man should be paid according to the amount over and above his own portion of the meal that he let the third traveler eat. Since three men had eaten eight loaves of bread, each man therefore consumed 8/3 loaves. One Samaritan had begun with 15/3 loaves, the other with 9/3 loaves. The first one then gave away 7/3, the second one 1/3—the ratios being seven to one.

7. There is no "other" dollar. Each man did in fact part with $9; the total spent was $27. Twenty-five dollars went to the motel, and the other $2 to the bellboy.

Answer to Magic Numbers

The reason for this magic is simple: when a three-digit number is repeated in sequence to form a six-digit "repetitive" number, the larger number is always 1,001 times the original number. Since 7 x 11 x 13 yields 1,001, dividing the long number by 7, 11, and 13 successively (in any order) will always yield the original number, regardless of the digits used.

Answers to Patented Pleasures

1. Cleverly-concealed cigars. **2.** Unique hunting decoy (with two men inside, making it the tallest cow in the world). **3.** Air-conditioned rocking chair. **4.** Excellent dancing partner. **5.** Sunshade (mounted on shoulder brackets, perhaps to avoid having to tip his hat). **6.** Sauna attachment (bather sits inside with head sticking out of round tank, while steam is piped in from front of tub).

Answers to Mystery Quiz

Maybe you've guessed by now what the quiz is all about. It's a tricky method of guessing how old you are by the names you give familiar objects— or in some cases, by finding out whether you remember the objects at all. With luck, your score will add up to your age. But chances are it will only come close. Here's how to total up:

A. If you answered Icebox, score 4; Ice Chest, score 6; Refrigerator, 2.

B. Anti-macassar or Tidy, 6; Doily, 3; no answer, 0.

C. Velocipede, 6; Tricycle, 4; Trike or Three-wheeler, 2.

D. Wristwatch, 4; Watch, 2. (Today "Wristwatch" is redundant. What other kinds are there?)

E. Pompadour, 4; any other answer or no answer, 1.

F. Bongo Drums or bongos, 2; any other answer or no answer, 4.

G. Plus-fours, 5; any other answer or no answer 2.

H. Talking-machine, 8; Gramophone or Graphophone, 7; Victrola, 6; Phonograph, 4; Record Player or Hi-Fi, 2; Stereo, 1.

I. Rumble seat, 4; any other answer, 0.

J. Billy, 5; Nightstick, 3; any other, 1.

K. Ice-cream Freezer or Maker, 4; any other answer or no answer, 1.

L. Four-in-hand, 4; any other answer or no answer, 1.

So add up your score. Did it come close? Well . . . if it didn't, you're pretty spry for your age, or else wise beyond your years!

Set in Optima, a light, open typeface designed by
Hermann Zapf which combines the grace of a
roman with the simplicity of a sans serif.
Printed on Hallmark Eggshell Book paper.
Illustrations in "Patented Pleasures" chapter
reproduced courtesy The Bettmann Archive.

Designed by Harald Peter.